The Boss

Pete Guppy

RISING ★ STARS

SURVIVAL

in associati

nas

Helping Everyo

NASEN Ho
Tamworth,

Rising Stars UK Ltd.
22 Grafton Street, London W1S 4EX
www.risingstars-uk.com

Text © Rising Stars UK Ltd.

The right of Pete Guppy to be identified as the author of this work has been asserted by him in accordance with the Copyright, Design and Patents Act, 1988.

Published 2009

Cover design: Roger Warham
Cover image: Glory/Alamy
Text design and typesetting: Roger Warham
Publisher: Gill Budgell
Editorial consultant: Lorraine Petersen

British Library Cataloguing in Publication Data.

A CIP record for this book is available from the British Library.

ISBN: 978-1-84680-598-1

Printed in the UK by CPI Bookmarque, Croydon, CR0 4TD

Mixed Sources
Product group from well-managed forests and other controlled sources
www.fsc.org Cert no. TT-COC-002227
© 1996 Forest Stewardship Council
FSC

Chapter

Joe looked to his left. Then he looked to his right. He was trapped.

The walls were too big to get over and the gang were closing in.

They were standing in a line across the road, walking slowly towards him. They didn't need to rush. They knew they had him trapped.

There were six of them. And they all looked bigger and older than him. There was only one thing to do. He ran at the gang and tried pushing past them.

It was no good. Strong arms stopped him and pushed him back against the wall.

"Not so fast. I want a word with you," said the leader of the gang.

"_____ off," said Joe.

The leader took off his sunglasses. He was much older than the others.

"Now look. There's an easy way of doing this, and there's a hard way. It's up to you," he said.

Joe was shaking with fear but he said, "Get lost. Leave me alone."

The gang leader got so close that Joe could smell he'd been drinking. He could also see a long scar on the man's face. It went from his chin, across his cheek, and over to his left ear.

Scarface looked mean and hard.

"I haven't seen you around here before. What's your name?" he asked.

Joe didn't say a word.

This time, Scarface prodded Joe in the chest with his finger. "I said, what's your name? And what are you doing on my patch?"

Joe looked at the scar. "My name's Joe. And I'm looking for my dad," he said.

"That's better. Now tell me more," said Scarface.

"My dad works on the boats. He should have come home two years ago. I've run away to look for him. I've got to get on a boat to Hong Kong," said Joe.

"And have you got a ticket to get on a boat to Hong Kong?" asked Scarface.

"No," said Joe.

"Have you got the cash to buy a ticket?" asked Scarface.

"No," said Joe.

"So how are you going to get to Hong Kong?" asked Scarface.

"I don't know. I haven't worked that out, yet," said Joe.

Scarface looked at the gang. "Well, Joe, this is your lucky day. I think I can help you," he said. Then he asked Joe two more questions:

"Do you need some food?"

"Yes," said Joe.

"Do you need a bed for the night?"

"Yes," said Joe.

"Well, I think we can do a deal. You come and work for me and I'll get you to Hong Kong. What do you say?" asked Scarface.

Joe didn't know what to say. He didn't like the look of this man. But he did want to find his dad. And he was hungry.

Scarface said, "Come on. We'll look

after you. We'll get you some food and show you where you can sleep."

Then he turned to the gang and said, "Take Joe to the flat and get him some fish and chips. I'll see you later."

Joe let himself be led along the road by the gang. He couldn't fight them, or outrun them. He needed food and sleep. And maybe Scarface would keep to his word.

As they went up the road they looked just like a set of lads having fun. But the truth isn't always easy to see.

They came out of the back street and turned left into a park. Some boys were playing football and the gang kicked their ball away as they walked across the pitch.

At the end of the park they took a path leading to a block of flats.

When they got there, one of the gang looked around. Then they rushed up to the main doors.

A mum with a pram opened the doors from the inside. The gang pushed past her and ran with Joe up the steps to the second floor.

One of the gang unlocked the door of number 38 and they all went in.

"Well, here we are. Home sweet home," he said to Joe.

And the door was slammed shut.

Chapter

The flat was a mess. There were empty cans and bottles all over the floor. Empty take-away boxes were piled up on the table and chairs.

Fish and chip papers had been rolled up into footballs and kicked around the room. And scraps of food had been left all over the place.

There were holes in the carpet where fag ends had been stubbed out. More fag ends had been piled up by the gas fire and some had been dropped into old mugs of tea. Socks and shoes were scattered all over the floor.

"Home, sweet home" didn't fit this flat at all. It didn't smell sweet. And it wasn't like home.

"You can sleep in here. The bed's mine, but you can have the mattress on the floor," said one of the gang.

Joe looked at the small bedroom. The mattress was under the window. And the window had bars across it.

"We haven't got more blankets. But I think The Boss will bring you a sleeping bag," said the lad.

"Who's The Boss?" asked Joe. The lad smiled and said, "You just met him. He's the one helping you get to Hong Kong."

"Scarface is a better name for him," said Joe.

"Don't ever call him that. Not if you don't want a scar as well. Just call him 'The Boss'. And do what he wants you to do," said the lad.

"And what's that? What do you lot do for him?" asked Joe.

"He'll tell you, later. I think the fish and chips have just got here," said the lad.

They had. Joe was soon stuffing himself full of the best fish and chips he had ever eaten. Then he had a bag of crisps and a can of drink.

He was just sitting back in his chair when The Boss came into the flat. He had a plastic bag in each hand.

"How are you feeling?" he asked Joe.

"OK, thanks," said Joe.

"Well here's something to make you feel even better," said The Boss.

He held up the two plastic bags.

"Which one do you want? The one in my right hand or the one in my left?" he asked.

"Left," said Joe. The Boss handed it over and Joe took out a sleeping bag.

"We can't have you getting cold at night, can we?" said The Boss. Then he handed the second bag to Joe and said, "This one's for you as well."

Joe opened the bag and took out a brand new leather jacket.

"It'll make you look cool on the street," said The Boss.

Joe opened his mouth to say thanks.

"No need for thanks. Like I said, it's your lucky day," said The Boss.

Then he took some cans of lager out of the fridge. He opened them up and gave them to the gang. He put one can next to Joe and asked, "Have you ever had a lager?"

"No," said Joe.

"Well it's time you started," said The Boss.

The Boss lifted his can in the air and said, "Let's drink to Joe getting to Hong Kong." All the gang took a drink, but Joe just looked at his can.

"Come on, give it a go," said The Boss. Joe took a sip.

"That's the way, Joe. It won't kill you. You'll soon get to like it," said one of them.

Joe took a bigger drink, but he breathed in at the same time and some of the lager went up his nose. The gang cheered.

The Boss patted him on the back and said, "Keep going, Joe. You'll get used to it."

Joe tried to stop spluttering and sneezing. The Boss said, "The flat's a bit messy but it's home to the gang. And it's your home as well, if you want to stay."

Joe looked around him. He'd been on the run for four days and been hungry and cold for most of the time. Now he was full of food and being given gifts.

The gang seemed happy. And The Boss said he could get him onto a boat to Hong Kong.

The Boss seemed to know what Joe was thinking.

"How much do you want to get to Hong Kong?" he asked.

"I've got to get there. I've got to find out what happened to my dad. My mum died years ago and now my dad's missing," said Joe. His eyes filled with tears.

The Boss smiled to himself.

"It's OK, Joe. I'll help you. Now have a drink and you'll feel better," he said.

Joe dried his eyes and had a swig of lager. He was feeling very tired and his head felt a bit fuzzy.

The Boss said, "All these lads have run away from home, Joe. They all want to get something out of life, and they're working to get it.

"If you want to get to Hong Kong, then you are going to have to work for it too. So, why don't you stay and work for me?"

Joe looked as if he was going to say something. But then he closed his eyes and fell asleep.

Chapter

3

It was the afternoon when Joe woke up.
There was no one in the flat. He made
himself a cup of tea and some toast.
This was better than being on the run.

He put on his new jacket and looked at
himself in the mirror. The Boss was right.
He did look cool.

Then he looked at the mess around him.

He took the mugs, cups and plates into the kitchen. Then he picked up the cans, bottles and fag ends and put them in a plastic bag That made the flat a bit more like home.

"Maybe that's what I should do. Make this my home and work for The Boss until he helps me get to Hong Kong," Joe said to himself.

He picked up the rubbish bag to take it outside. But when he tried to open the door of the flat, it was locked.

There wasn't a key. And all the windows had bars across them. He was locked in! Was this going to be his home or his prison?

He turned on the TV and sat down to watch it. Then he turned it off and walked round the flat. He was restless. So he did some more clearing up.

That's when he began smiling to himself. Here he was, clearing up a room without having to be told. His mum would have loved it. He could still hear her saying, "If you put your toys away, I'll read you a story." He'd been five years old when she'd said that.

By the time he was six, she was dead. His dad had looked after him, but he worked at sea and was away from home a lot. That's why he'd been living with Mr and Mrs Barker.

It was OK at first. His dad sent them money and letters every month. Then they got a letter from Hong Kong saying he had a new job that paid a lot more money.

But then the letters stopped. And the Barkers got angry about not getting the money. So he'd run away to look for his dad.

His plan had been to get to Liverpool. And then get to Hong Kong by boat. But he couldn't get to Liverpool because the police were looking for him.

He'd slept in a cave but a gang found him and stole all his money and camping things. Then one of the gang had died in a shop fire.

The police thought it was Joe who had been killed, and they stopped looking for him. So he got on the train to Liverpool.

Now The Boss had found him, and here he was, sitting in a flat looking at a locked door.

All he could do was wait.

At last, a key went into the lock and the gang burst into the room.

They put take-away food on the table. And took cans of lager out of plastic bags. Music was put on.

The empty flat was now bursting with life. It put a smile on Joe's face.

"Come on, Joe. Grab some food. We've got a Chinese take-away tonight," said one of the gang.

The Boss came in and said, "Just think, Joe. If you come and work for me and get to Hong Kong, you can have real Chinese food. You can sit and eat it with your dad."

Joe smiled and grabbed some of the food. Then he helped himself to a can of lager.

"That's it, you're one of us now," said one of the gang.

"Well? Are you going to stay and work for me?" asked The Boss.

"What is it you do?" asked Joe.

"I help kids have a good time. I get them things they want," said The Boss.

"What things?" asked Joe.

The Boss opened up his left hand and showed Joe some small white pills.

"These things," he said.

"What are they?" asked Joe.

"I call them Happy Pills. They're a bit like the lager you're drinking. They help you have a good time," said The Boss.

"You mean drugs. I don't do drugs," said Joe.

The Boss smiled and said, "Trust me. They don't harm you. They're not the hard stuff." The Boss put the pills in his pocket.

Then he said, "Look, Joe. All you have to do is find me some kids who want some fun. Kids in the park, kids coming out of school, kids in McDonald's. Just hang around asking questions. Then, if they want some pills, tell them you can get them some."

One of the gang came up and said, "It's easy. We'll show you how to do it."

The Boss said, "If you want to get to Hong Kong, you need my help. You can't just walk onto a ship without being seen. But I can fix it for you. Work for me, and I'll get you on a ship."

The Boss held out his hand. "Is it a deal?" he asked.

Joe didn't want to push drugs. But he did want to find his dad. "It's a deal," he said.

Chapter

4

The gang came over and patted Joe on the back.

"This seems like a good time to have a bit of fun," said The Boss. And there in his open hand were six white pills.

"Take one if you want one," he said. Each of the gang took one. That left one pill. Everyone was looking at Joe.

"Go on, give it a go. It's just a bit of fun. Don't be the odd one out," said The Boss.

Joe looked at the pill. He didn't want to be left out. He was fed up with being on his own. He wanted to be part of a family.

So, like the rest of his new family, he picked up the pill and put it in his mouth. Then he took a drink from his can.

The Boss looked pleased. "I'm proud of you," he said to Joe. Joe didn't know how he felt about himself.

The Boss said it would be all right, but what would his dad have said? Joe went and sat in his room.

"Cheer up. It's happy time," said one of the gang.

But Joe sat on his mattress and tried to think. Maybe he could bring the pill back by making himself sick.

He stuck his fingers down his throat but it was no good.

All he could do now was wait and see what it did to him.

He didn't have to wait long. His feelings of fear soon left him. He started to smile and feel happy. He felt safe and warm. He was floating on big white fluffy clouds made of cotton wool. He knew everything in his life was going to be OK.

He would get to Hong Kong and his dad would be waiting for him. They would hug each other.

Joe had never been so happy. He liked the flat. He liked the gang of lads. And he liked The Boss. He even grinned at the bars on the windows of his bedroom.

Joe was still grinning as one of the lads led him out of the bedroom.

The gang smiled at him.

"Well, Joe. Did you have a good trip?" one of them asked.

Joe's brain wasn't working very well.

"What trip? I haven't been on holiday," he said. The gang started laughing.

"He thinks 'trip' means holiday," said one of the gang. So they took it in turns to make fun of him.

"Did you bring us a stick of rock back from your trip?"

"Did you spend your time getting stoned?"

"Or were you puffing on a weed?"

"Or having some coke?"

Joe didn't know why they were laughing so much. But he kept on smiling at them.

"You must be a dope. You'll get a smack if you don't see it soon," said one of them.

Joe still didn't get it. Just as the gang stopped laughing, one of them said, "If you don't get it soon, I'm going to crack up." And that started them off again. Joe still didn't see the joke, but he was happy. He had a new home and a new family.

He was at the best party he'd ever been to.
And everything was going to be OK.
But then the party came to an end.

From floating on clouds of happiness he came crashing down with a thud.

He started feeling dizzy. Then he started shaking. He got pains in his chest. And he was sick all over his bed. Then he was sick again on the way to the toilet. He stayed on the toilet feeling as if his guts were dropping out.

Joe had never felt as bad as this in all his life. He needed help.

The next morning, The Boss was there to help him!

"Just take this. It'll make you feel better," he said. So Joe took the pill. And up he went to having that blanket of happiness all around him.

But then down he came again to the shakes, shivers and shits.

Joe was starting to become hooked on drugs. And The Boss was there to help him on his way.

Chapter 5

After a week in the flat, Joe knew all the gang. There was Slim, Blue, Ratty, The Hulk and Snow White. Real names were never used.

Slim was just the right name for him. He was a big, fat lad who ate lots of food! And he ate it fast. When he finished his meal he went round begging or stealing from the others. That sometimes ended in a fight. He nicked some chips from Ratty one night and got a fork stuck in his hand.

But Slim was good fun. He told rude jokes and played games on the computer.

Blue spent most of his life watching TV. He sometimes sat up all night. The gang said he was the only 16 year-old who still watched Blue Peter.

Blue had rings in his nose and ears, and his head was shaved. It made him look hard but he was an easy-going lad.

Ratty wasn't easy-going. He looked hard, and was hard. He was the smallest of the gang and the meanest. He had a short temper and it was best to stay away from him.

He was 16 but looked as if he needed to shave twice a day. He didn't say much. But when he did speak, the rest of the gang listened to him.

He spent a lot of money on trainers and sunglasses. He smoked a lot, and some of his fags had a funny smell to them.

The Hulk liked smells. He liked splashing after shave over himself before he went out with one of his girlfriends. He loved chatting up girls. He was good at it.

He'd say things like, "I want money, girls and a good time. And it starts right now." He spent lots of money on clothes and was always well dressed. He also spent a long time in the bathroom checking that he looked cool.

Snow White never looked cool. But he did spend a lot of time in the bathroom. That's where he snorted the white powder he just had to have.

It was a drug that had taken over his life. He looked ill all the time and his hands shook when he picked things up. He was moody and seemed to live in a world of his own.

And then there was The Boss. He was about ten years older than the rest of the gang. He came to the flat driving a big flash car. He was a like the Pied Piper, always telling the lads he was leading them to a better life.

He paid them for their work and sometimes gave them gifts as well. He was The Boss all right. They all seemed a bit afraid of him. Even Ratty did as he was told.

But The Boss didn't live in the flat, so Joe didn't see much of him.

It was the gang he spent time with. And he got to like some of them. The longer he stayed, the more he felt like one of them. One by one they told him how they had got into drugs.

"All my friends were into drugs, so I didn't want to be left out," said Slim.

"I was bored, I just did it for a laugh," said Ratty.

"My older sister started, so I did as well," said Blue.

"My baby-sitter gave me some," said The Hulk.

"Me and my mates tried some as a bet. I got hooked," said Snow White.

They all told Joe how easy it was to work for The Boss. "All you have to do is hang around and talk to kids. Just tell them that if they want to try some pills, you know the man who can help them. The Boss will do the rest," said Blue.

"That's right," said Slim. "If you keep getting kids to take pills, The Boss will be happy. And if he's happy, then you'll get what you want."

"And if you don't do this job, somebody else will," said Ratty.

"The kids don't have to take the pills if they don't want to. So you're not harming them," said The Hulk.

"Not harming them," Joe said to himself.

He knew that wasn't true. He knew what the pills were doing to him. So why was he going to help The Boss push drugs?

He had to. How else was he going to get to Hong Kong?

Chapter

"Come on. It's your first day at school," said Slim. He rushed Joe out of the flat and onto the streets. Joe was starting his new job.

"Where are we going?" he asked

"I told you. We're off to school. We're going to hang around outside the gates until the kids come out at dinner-time," said Slim.

And that's what they did. Joe stood and watched as Slim spoke to some of the kids as they came out.

Then Slim came back to him and said, "I told you this was an easy job. I've just got a new kid for The Boss."

"Which one?" asked Joe.

"The little one over there. He's with two mates," said Slim.

Joe looked across at a boy kicking a can along the ground. He looked about ten years old.

"Come on," said Slim. "It's best not to stay in one place too long. Let's go to McDonald's."

Slim spoke to more kids as they ate burgers and chips. Then he and Joe went to the park. Then back to the school gates for home-time.

"Not a bad day's work," said Slim, as they walked back to the flat.

"That's two new ones for The Boss. That puts me in his good books."

"What happens if you get into his bad books?" asked Joe.

Slim stopped and said, "Don't. He's got a bad temper and he can turn nasty. And don't run off. I've seen him beat up lads who have run out on him. Just do what he wants you to do."

Joe could see the fear in Slim's eyes.

Then Slim smiled and said, "Let's go back and have a game on the computer." They played three games. And Joe still couldn't beat him. The Boss came to the flat, and Slim got paid for his day's work.

He looked at Joe and asked, "Is there anything you want?" Joe nodded and The Boss gave him a pill.

The next day he went out with Slim again. They went to a school about a mile away.

"It's your turn today. Try and make friends. You'll get the hang of it," said Slim.

Joe gave it a go. But the kids just walked past him. They went to a fish and chip shop where some kids were hanging about. Joe tried again but they told him to push off.

Slim said, "OK. That's it for today. You'll soon get better at it. Come on, let's go and see some of Liverpool."

And off they went to walk the streets.

Joe saw posh-looking shops, big blocks of flats and new cars. He also saw people sleeping on the streets and begging for money.

They went back to the flat. The Boss came round again and asked how Joe had got on. Slim told him. The Boss went over to Joe.

"Not a good first day, Joe. I hope you have better luck tomorrow."

The Boss had a smile on his face, but the words sounded cold. Joe felt a chill go down his back.

Then The Boss gave him a pill. And for a short time, everything felt better.

But then the shivers started, and every part of his body seemed to hurt.

The bad times were lasting longer than the good. But he couldn't do without the good times.

Joe spent the night asking himself the question, "Is the rest of my life going to be like this?"

Chapter

7

It was lunch-time. Joe and Slim were outside the school gates and Joe was getting some help.

Slim said, "See the girl over there? She's the sister of a lad who gets pills from The Boss. I think she wants to take them as well. Go and talk to her. She knows I work for The Boss." Joe went over to her.

"Do you know The Boss?" she asked.

"Yes," said Joe.

"Can you get me some pills? My brother says I'm too young. But I want them for a party," she said.

Joe stood looking at her. A party! That's how he'd started. She didn't know what she was getting herself into. These pills weren't sweets. These pills could mess up your life. As Joe looked at her, something seemed to snap inside his head.

He couldn't do it! He couldn't push drugs. He wanted to find out about his dad, but not like this.

He looked around him. If he was going to run, this was the time to do it. He knew he could run faster than Slim, but what about The Boss?

Joe looked at the girl, and said, "Don't do it." And then he was off and running.

Slim saw him go.

"Don't do it. You can't get away!"
he shouted.

But Joe wasn't listening. He was running. He ran past the school, along a path, and into some side streets.

His lungs were on fire and his legs felt like jelly. He had to stop and rest. What was the matter with him? He was better at running than this.

"It must be the pills," he said to himself.

Joe put his hands on his knees. He had to get away as fast as he could, but he wasn't going to do it by running.

He tried to think. He couldn't get a bus because he didn't have any money. He couldn't go to the police in case they found out he was on drugs. So what could he do? And how long did he have before Slim called The Boss on his mobile?

Joe stood up. He saw Ratty at the end of the street.

He was smiling that nasty smile of his.

"Now, what are you doing here all by yourself? Going for a run, are you?" Ratty shouted.

Joe was off like a frightened rabbit. He ran into a street full of shops, looking for somewhere to hide.

Then he saw a boy get off his bike on the other side of the road. The boy was just about to lock it up when Joe dashed across the road. He pushed the boy out of the way and jumped on the bike.

Ratty was catching up with him and the traffic lights were on red. Joe went through the red lights and two cars almost hit him. There was a screech of brakes and hooting of horns. Everyone turned to look.

But Joe just pushed down harder on the pedals. He looked round to see if Ratty was still coming after him, but he wasn't.

Joe didn't know where he was going. He turned left past more shops and then past a park. It was hard work but he started to smile. It felt good to be getting away.

He slowed down as he went up a steep hill. His lungs were hurting and his legs begged him to stop. But he kept going until he got to the top.

He was gasping for air as he got off the bike. He dragged it onto a bit of grass by the side of the road and flopped down beside it. That was when a car pulled up next to him.

"Nice try, Joe. Now get in the car."

Joe looked up to see The Boss grinning at him. The back door of the car opened and Joe saw Ratty and Blue sitting there.

"Come on, Joe. There's room in here for one more," said Ratty.

All three were grinning. They had him trapped again.

Joe didn't have long to think. Maybe there was no getting away from The Boss. Maybe he had to get used to the life of pushing drugs. Maybe it was the only way to get to Hong Kong.

Or would he end up like the kids he had seen on the streets?

Sick-looking kids with dark sunken eyes in thin faces. Some sleeping in doorways. All begging for money to buy more drugs.

"Are you getting in the car, or do I have to come and get you?" asked The Boss.

Chapter

8

Joe looked at the mean-looking face with the scar across it. His mind was made up. He was back on the bike in a flash and going down a grassy bank as fast as he could.

He didn't know what was at the bottom of the bank. But he was getting away from the car.

Ratty and Blue came running after him but The Boss called them back. The chase was on, again. Joe knew that if he didn't get away this time, he might never get away at all.

As Joe came down the steep bank he saw a path. It was where an old railway line had been. Bikes could get along it but not cars. Joe's brakes were full on as he skidded and bumped his way onto the path. But which way? Left or right?

Left took him back into Liverpool, to where the chase had started. So he had to go right.

But hang on. If he was going to get away from this gang, he had to start thinking like them. What would they expect him to do? And what were they doing right now?

Joe knew that Ratty and Blue would still be watching him.

They would be waiting to see which way he went. Then they could grab him if the path came close to a road.

Well, he was going to try and trick them. Joe turned to the right. This was the way the gang would expect him to go.

He gave them time to get back into the car, then stopped and turned round. Now he was going back to where the chase had first started.

He was taking a big risk. But it would take time for the gang to find out they had been tricked. And he needed that time to look for a way off the path. Then he could find a way out of Liverpool without being seen by the gang.

But he didn't have much time. The Boss would soon be back looking for him. And he wouldn't be pleased.

Joe rode as fast as he could. But he couldn't see a way off the path.

And now there was a wall of rock on each side of him.

He was feeling trapped again.

"There has to be a gap soon," he said to himself. But the rock walls just went on and on. However fast he went, he still couldn't get free of them. Was he going to have walls around him for the rest of his life?

His legs were now screaming at him to stop. But he wasn't listening to them. Fear kept them working.

At last, the rock walls came to an end. Joe had a shock, just ahead of him was the river Mersey.

He stopped and gulped some air into his lungs. Now he knew where this path was going. It was going to the docks.

The path used to be the railway line the trains used when they took the cargo to, and from, the ships.

But getting this close to the docks wasn't helping him get out of Liverpool. Was it best to go on? Or go back?

It was a long way back to where he'd got onto the path. And what if some of the gang were coming after him on bikes?

Joe was also feeling very tired. It would soon be dark, and he needed somewhere to hide for the night. But where could he go?

As he looked at the docks, his dad came into his mind. His dad must have seen all of this each time he came to Liverpool to get onto a ship.

His job was to take the cargo all over the world. It could be food, wood, wool, oil, grain, or even cars.

All along the docks stood the sheds where the cargo was kept before it was put onto ships. Not garden sheds. These sheds were as long as a football pitch and taller than a house.

Some were still in use, but some were empty. Then Joe saw the letters P&R on the side of one of the sheds. P&R was the name of the shipping line his dad had worked for. The shed looked empty.

The more he looked at the letters, the more they acted like a magnet. That's where he was going to hide for the night. He felt it was taking him closer to his dad.

As Joe got closer, he could see that bits of the wooden shed were falling down.

There was no one around so he rode round the back looking for a way in. A window was open. He got in and opened a door from the inside. Then he got his bike inside and shut the door. He felt safer now.

Stepping into this dark shed was like going back in time. It had an old musty smell about it. There was no cargo left but there were empty boxes and big rolls of cloth.

Cobwebs hung across the room and over the windows. A lot of men had worked in this shed in the past. Now only the spiders had work to do.

Joe looked down at his bike. He had to hide it, then himself. Then he saw the mud on the wheels. He must have left tracks outside!

He opened the door a little and looked out. There was still no one around.

He rubbed out the tracks as best he could and got back into the shed.

Joe hid his bike by putting boxes on top of it. Now he had to hide himself and get some rest.

It was getting dark but he could just see some stairs going up to the next floor. They didn't look safe but he wanted to get upstairs if he could.

He would see more from an upstairs window when morning came.

Joe went up slowly, step by step. Some steps were rotten and gave way. He held onto the wall but the staircase began to sway from side to side.

He felt hot and his hands were wet with sweat.

He was pleased to get to the top. But now every bit of his body was hurting. He had pains in his head and chest, and his hands were still wet with sweat.

He felt ill.

"I just need some sleep," he said to himself.

He made a bed out of a sack and some cloth. Then he put boxes around it. "I'm safe. No one knows I'm here," he said. And he closed his eyes.

But it wasn't sleep that Joe was drifting into to. He was drifting into something much more deadly than that. He was taking the long, dark trip into a coma.

His brain was saying, "You've been hit by drugs, fear and a long chase.
That's too much for you to deal with. I'm shutting down to stop the pain."

Joe didn't wake up when the birds started singing. He didn't wake up when the sun came up.

He stayed locked in a coma. And he was right. No one knew where he was.

Chapter 9

Joe's eyes flickered as he came out of the dark world of his coma.

"Well, Joe. Did you have a good trip?"

They were the same words the gang had said to him in the flat!

But as Joe blinked open his eyes, it wasn't The Boss, or Ratty, or Blue he was looking at.

"Well, are you going to say something to your old dad?"

Joe didn't say a word. He just flung his arms round his dad's neck and hung on as tightly as he could. If this was a dream, he wanted it to go on forever.

"It's OK, Joe. You're not dreaming. You've been in a coma. But you've come out of it now," said his dad.

Joe tried to speak, but all that came out were big sobs and floods of tears.

His dad didn't let go of him. He held onto Joe and said, "It's OK. I'll never leave you again. Never."

They stayed hugging each other for a long time. Then someone said, "I think Joe needs some rest now, Mr Robbins. You can see him again in the morning."

Joe looked to see who was speaking. It was a nurse. And for the first time he saw that he was in a hospital bed.

Then he saw the tubes sticking in his arms. His dad said, "You've been in here for six weeks, Joe. The tubes have helped you stay alive."

"Six weeks! What do you mean, six weeks?" said Joe.

"You've been in a coma for six weeks. You've been very ill. We've been waiting all this time for you to open your eyes," said his dad.

The nurse came up to the bed. "That's all the talk you two are doing for now. It's time you went, Mr Robbins," she said.

She turned to Joe. "And are you going to get some sleep?" she asked.

"But I've just had a long sleep," said Joe.

His dad and the nurse smiled at each other. "Yes, I know. But this time we know you'll wake up," said the nurse.

His dad let go of Joe's hand and stood up. "I'll see you in the morning," he said.

He left the room. And the nurse tucked Joe in for the night.

"Will I go back into a coma if I shut my eyes?" he asked the nurse.

"No. And we'll all be here waiting for you when you wake up in the morning," she said.

The nurse was right. When Joe woke up the next morning, his dad was there by his bedside.

"Can we go home now?" asked Joe.

"Not yet. They need to keep a check on you for a few days. Then we can go home," said his dad.

Joe sat up in bed. "I've got something to tell you, Dad," he said.

"Go on then," said his dad.

"I've been taking drugs," said Joe.

"I know you have. They almost killed you," said his dad.

"And I stole a bike," said Joe.

"I know," said his dad.

"And I stole some money from Mr Barker," said Joe.

"I know," said his dad.

His dad sat on the bed and put his arm around Joe. "We can sort all this out," he said.

"I was just trying to find you," said Joe, with tears in his eyes.

"I know you were. But we found you first, thank God," said his dad.

"How did you find me?" asked Joe.

His dad said, "I came back to England a week after you'd run away from the Barkers. The police told me it wasn't you who had died in the fire. They knew you were trying to get to Liverpool so that's where we started looking.

"Then the police were told about a boy stealing a bike, and the same boy was seen being chased onto a path.

"We went up and down the path hoping to find you. At last we came to the docks.

"I saw the big P&R letters on one of the long sheds. I somehow knew you might be there. And you were, curled up like a mouse in winter."

"So you found me. And The Boss didn't," said Joe.

"What Boss?" asked his dad.

Joe told him all about it.

"I'll tell the police. You can go over it again with them when you feel better," said his dad.

"And if you are going to get better, you need your rest," said the nurse.

"OK, nurse. I can take a hint. I'm off," said his dad.

"But Dad, you haven't told me where you've been for the last two years," said Joe.

"I'll tell you tomorrow," said his dad.

As Joe snuggled down into his bed he felt safe and very happy.

But he still had one more shock waiting for him.

Chapter

His dad was by his bedside when he woke up the next day. Joe's first words were, "Where have you been for the last two years?"

His dad looked away from him. "I've been in prison," he said.

Joe's mouth fell open. "You've what?" he said.

His dad looked at him this time.

"I've been locked up for over two years in a prison in China," he said.

Joe's mouth was still open. "Why were you locked up?" he asked.

Joe's dad said, "For being a fool. I told you in my last letter that I had a new job. Well, I'd met a man who asked me to sail a small boat from Hong Kong to the mainland of China. He said he would pay me good money to take books, DVDs and CDs from Hong Kong to China. He said they sold very well over there.

"Well, I fell for it. He was looking for a greedy fool and he found me. I just wanted to make lots of money as fast as I could."

"So what happened?" asked Joe.

His dad said, "I sailed the boat for about six weeks. But I got the feeling that something wasn't right. When I checked some of the boxes I found drugs.

"That's why I was being paid so much money to do the job. I was working for a gang of drug smugglers."

Joe's mouth fell open again. "What did you do?" he asked.

"I went to the police, but they locked me up. They said it was so the gang couldn't get me. But I think the police felt I knew there were drugs on my boat. They kept me locked up for over two years."

"But why did you stop sending letters to us?" asked Joe.

"They wouldn't let letters go out of the prison. All I could do was wait and hope. In the end they let me go. As soon as I got back home the Barkers told me you had run away. So I came looking for you," said his dad.

"So we've both been mixed up with drugs," said Joe.

"Yes. And we've both been very lucky," said his dad.

"Can we go home now?" asked Joe.

A voice said, "No you can't. It will be two more days." It was the nurse who seemed to hear everything that was going on.

Over the next two days, Joe was told a few more things.

The doctors told him that he had been in the shed for about three days before his dad found him.

The police came and told him they had found the flat he'd been in, but it was empty.

The gang had moved on. But someone had called the police with a tip-off about a man dealing in drugs.

The police showed Joe a picture of the man they had picked up.

"That's him. That's The Boss," said Joe.

The police had found drugs on him. They said he would go to prison for a long time.

Joe couldn't help smiling.

Now it was The Boss who would end up looking at bars.

But who had given the police the tip-off? Joe hoped it was one of the gang who was trying to get out of drugs.

And his dad told him about the new job he had just got. It was on dry land, so his sailing days were over.

At last, it was time to go home. Joe and his dad thanked the doctors and nurses. The nurse that Joe's dad had nicknamed 'Big Ears' gave Joe a big hug and a kiss. Joe went bright red, but he gave her a hug as well.

Just as they were going, a doctor came up to Joe and said, "It will take a few weeks before you feel strong again. Here are some pills in case you feel dizzy over the next day or two."

"No thanks," said Joe. "I don't take pills."

Joe's story begins in

Runaway

Turn the page for a preview . . .

SURVIVAL

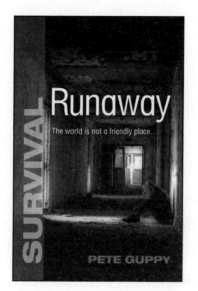

SURVIVAL

Runaway

The world is not a friendly place...

PETE GUPPY

"Stop nagging me!" yelled Joe.

"I'm not nagging you," said Mrs Barker.

"Yes, you are, so shut up," said Joe, as he ran up the stairs to his bedroom.

Mrs Barker came to the bottom of the stairs and shouted, "What did you say to me?"

Joe stopped at the top of the stairs and looked back.

"I said, stop nagging me. My dad never nagged me like you do!" he shouted.

Then he slammed the door of his bedroom.

Mrs Barker ran up the stairs and pushed open the bedroom door. "Well, you are not living with your dad. You are living with us. So just do as you are told," she said.

Joe was sitting on his bed. He was holding a bottle and looking at the ship that was inside it.

"Just shut up and leave me alone," he said.

Mrs Barker went red in the face. "How dare you speak to me like that? Just wait until I tell Mr Barker when he gets home from work. He'll deal with you. And you know what that means!"

Then she slammed the door and went downstairs.

"Now I'll get a telling off from Barker. And I might get a slap as well," said Joe to himself.

He sat thinking about why he was living with the Barkers at all. He was there because his mum was dead and his dad was away at sea.

"Where was his dad? Why had his letters stopped coming? Why hadn't he come back home?"

There was one question Joe didn't want to ask. "Was his dad still alive?"

Tears began to fill his eyes. He told himself to stop thinking like that. He knew what he had to do.

He had to get away from this house and go looking for his dad . . .

Look out for other exciting stories in the
Survival series:

Runaway

The Boss

The Gambling Habit

Stormy Waters

Flirting with Danger

Fireproof

Why Me?

Jet Scream

About the author

Have you ever been hunted by the police, chased by a gang, or tried to stay alive after a plane crash?

If you have, then you know the name of the game is survival. If you haven't, why not read about the teenagers in my stories. They find getting into trouble is easy. It's the getting out of trouble that's the hard bit.

I spent three years training to be a teacher and 33 years being one. I always wanted to know how hard it would be to write books for teenagers. Now I know!

Pete Guppy

SURVIVAL